Sharp keys

On the Meadow . . .

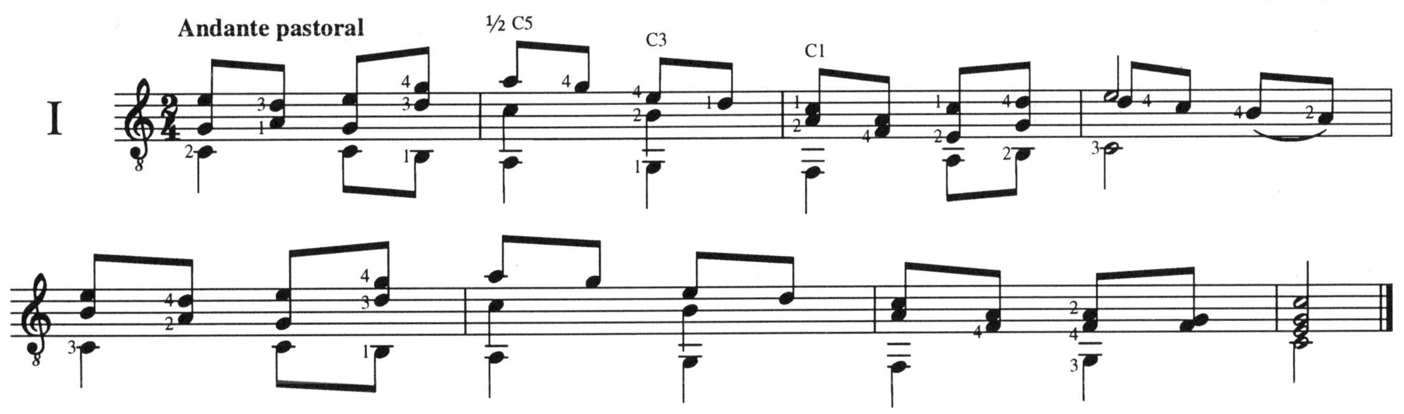

. . . Wildflowers nod in bright agreement to the sun and to the fragrant summer breezes blowing softly over the prairie.

View From a Hill . . .

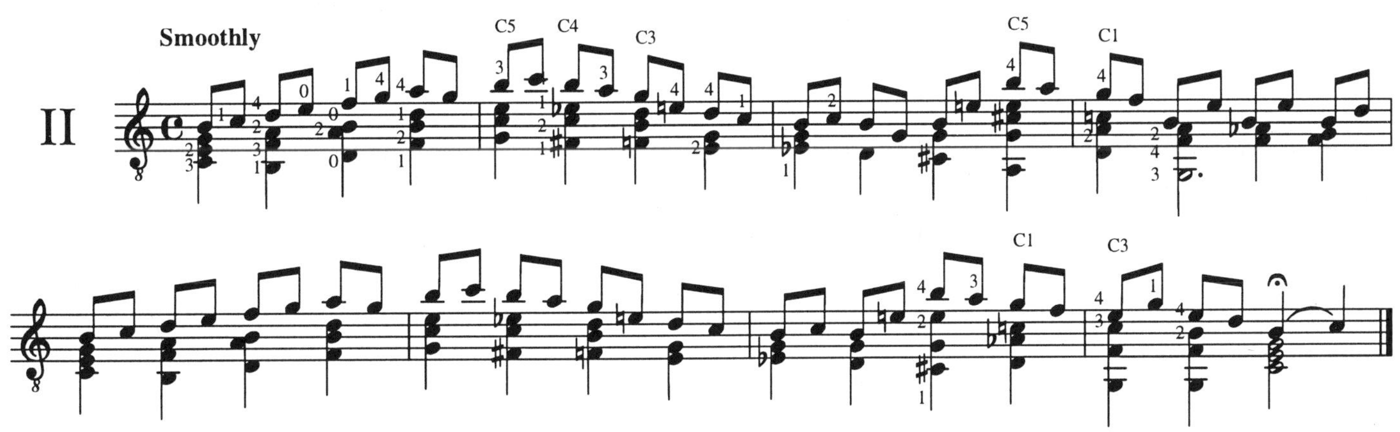

. . . The highest point for many miles overlooks a distant sea of golden wheat, and nearby green pastures surround a cobalt blue pond which mirrors the summer sky.

Fond Farewell . . .

. . . Once familiar places from long ago, revisited, to find they are gone or so changed that one must say "so long" to a fond retrospection.

Holiday . . .

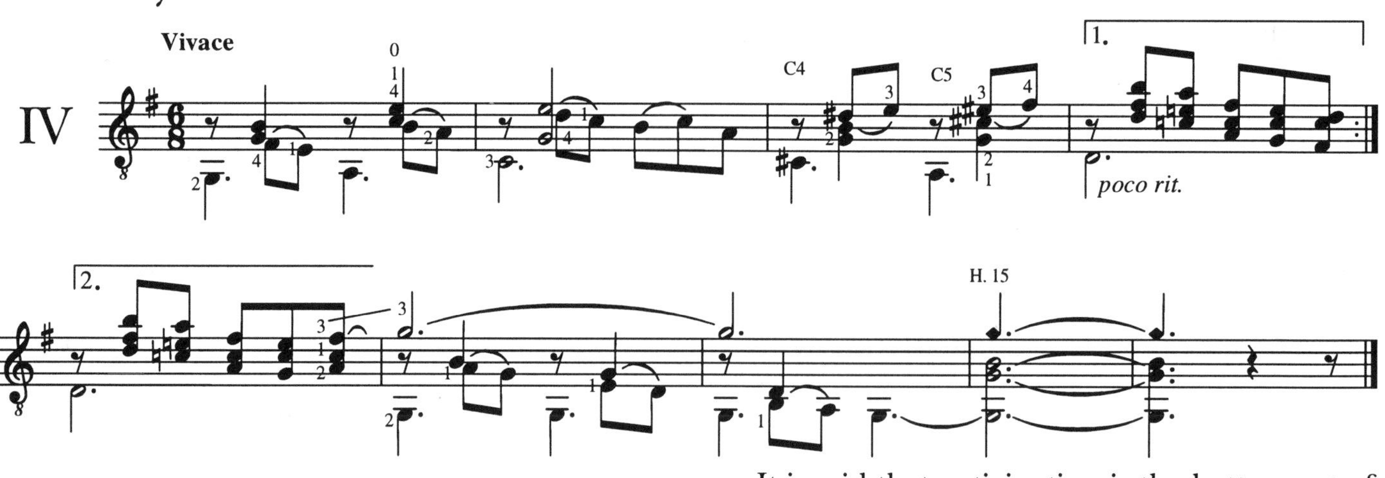

. . . It is said that anticipation is the better part of those brief excursion that seem to end, suddenly.

A Summer Garden . . .

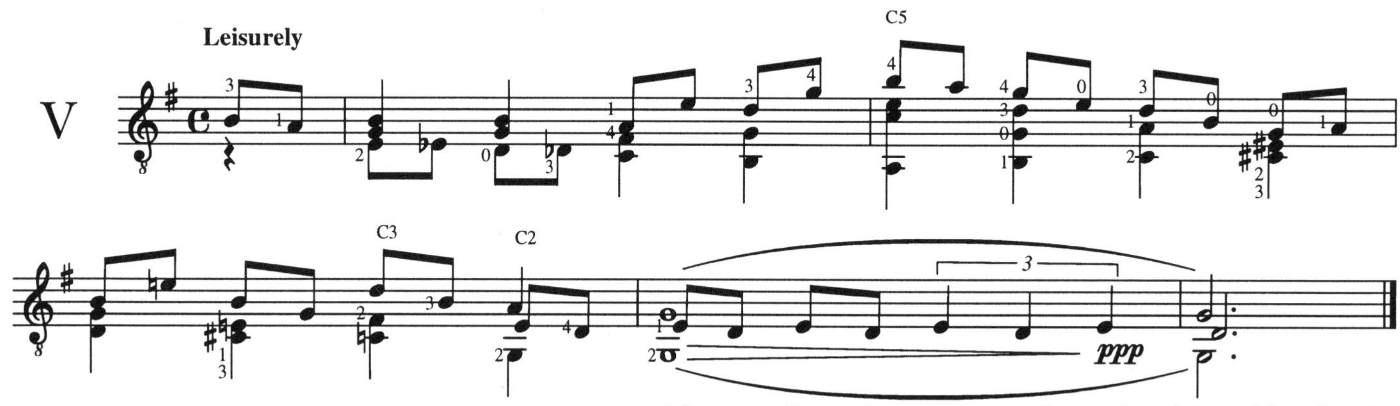

. . . It's a small garden—a row of purple phlox, blue bachelor buttons, and bright yellow sundrops - yet it seems to unfold into an acre of fragrance and color.

On a Frescobaldi Theme . . .

. . . The theme of the Frescobaldi Variations readily lends itself to improvisations in many harmonic styles and melodic inventions.

Butterflies . . .

. . . Spectacular swallow-tails, especially, whose brilliant colors rival and even surpass the flowers over which they hover.

Quiet Cove . . .

. . . A restful maneuvre is to allow a canoe to drift into a leafy cove to startle frogs on lily pads and basking turtles on half-submerged tree trunks.

Abandoned Farm . . .

. . . An enveloping melancholy seems to pervade over barn and shed, and the house itself appears lonely and forlorn.

Dancing Snowflakes. . .

. . . The first flakes of winter snow come swirling on the wind like feathery down.

The following four pieces; viz., Interlude XI, Interlude XII, The Pine Grove Prelude, and Interlude XIII may be combined in any desired order to form a miniature suite.

The Bird Sanctuary . . .

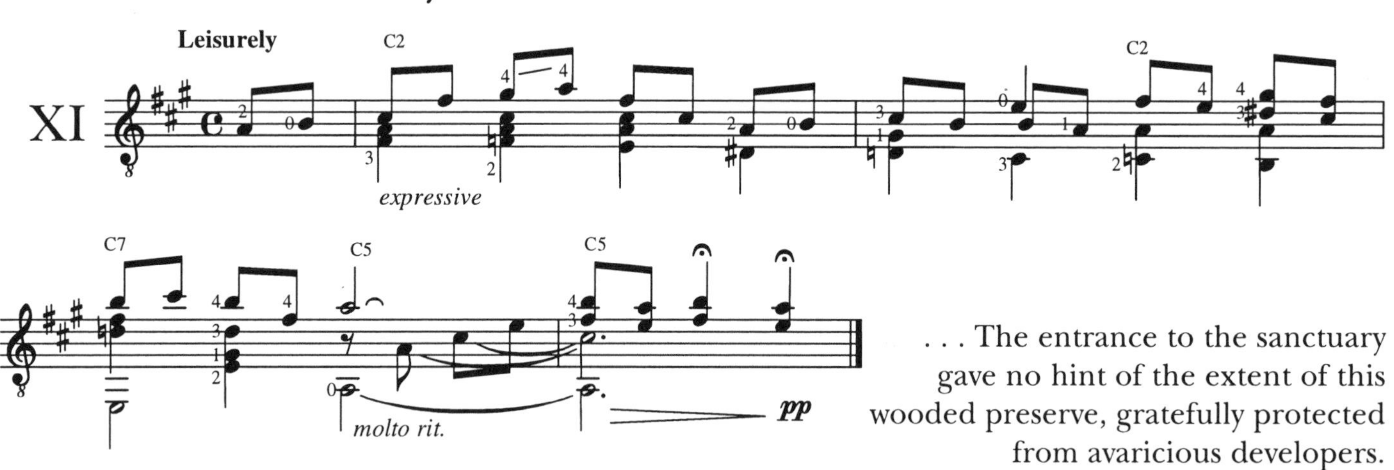

. . . The entrance to the sanctuary gave no hint of the extent of this wooded preserve, gratefully protected from avaricious developers.

Strolling the Path Ways . . .

The Sanctuary (2)

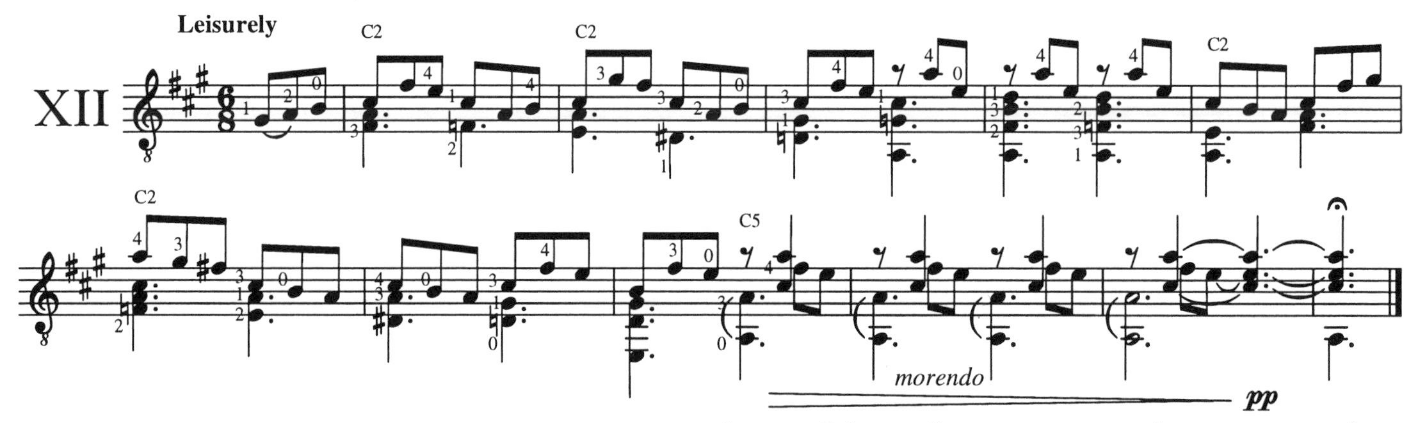

. . . Some of the trails were groomed to accommodate equestrian usage and smaller paths wound in secluded groves of deciduous and coniferous trees.

The Pine Grove . . .

The Sanctuary (3)

. . . The fragrance of pine is immediately evident and the soft bed of pine needles provide a soft cushion underfoot. Here, we linger awhile, before meandering on.

The Arbor . . .

The Sanctuary (4)

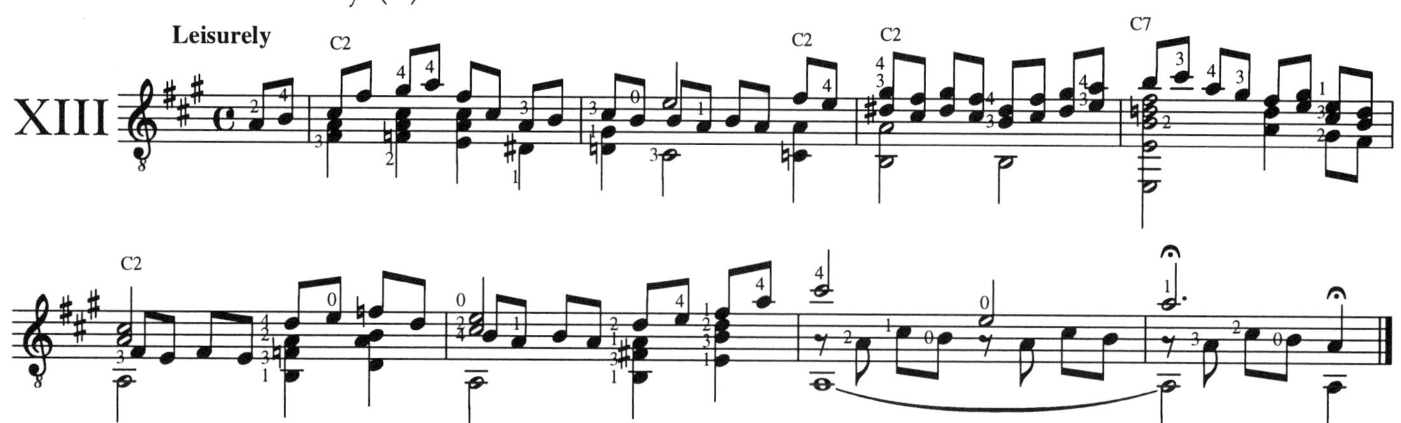

. . . None can better describe the effect nature has on one's equanimity than Ralph Waldo Emerson in a passage from *Nature.* "The incommunicable trees begin to persuade us to live with them, and quit our life of solemn trifles."

Emphatic Trifles . . .

. . . How often promising enterprises begin with much bustle and buzz and end in chagrin.

Sundrops . . .

. . . The Oenothera fructicosa is a hardy native American plant whose brilliant yellow clusters of flowers atop two foot high stems are so aptly describes as drops of sun.

Hyacinths . . .

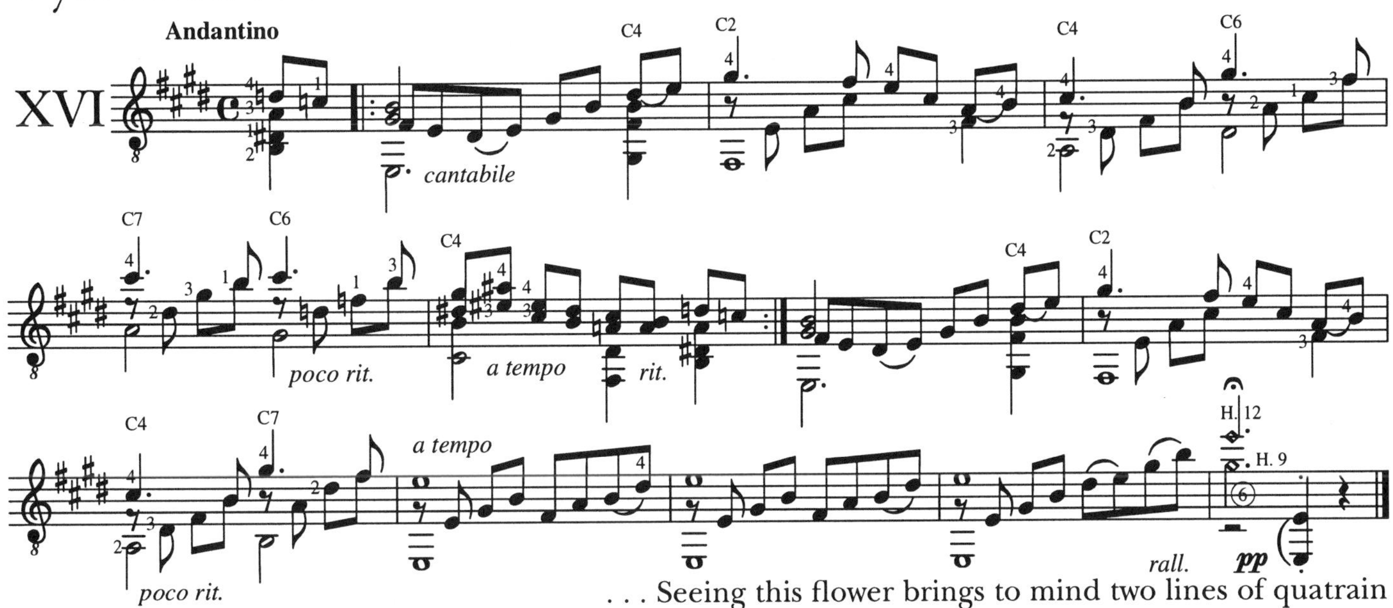

. . . Seeing this flower brings to mind two lines of quatrain (XIX) in Omar Khayyam's Rubaiyat; viz., That every Hyacinth the Garden wears, Dropt in her lap from some once lovely head.

Poem . . .

. . . No particular poem is this, but an accumulation of many great verses which blend together bringing color and rhythm to mundane affairs.

The Pavilion . . .

Note: play the bass voice throughout with a "semi-staccato" touch, i.e., each quarter note receiving 2/3 of the beat. The right thumb dampens the string with a delayed action, an effect characteristic of "baroque" and "swing, Jazz" styles of bass playing.

. . . From across the inlet come the first sounds of music as vacationers converge for an evening of lake-side ballroom dancing.

On the Carousel . . .

. . . The sight and sound of a merry-go-round have a special and magical appeal for children of all ages.

The Blue Bicycle . . .

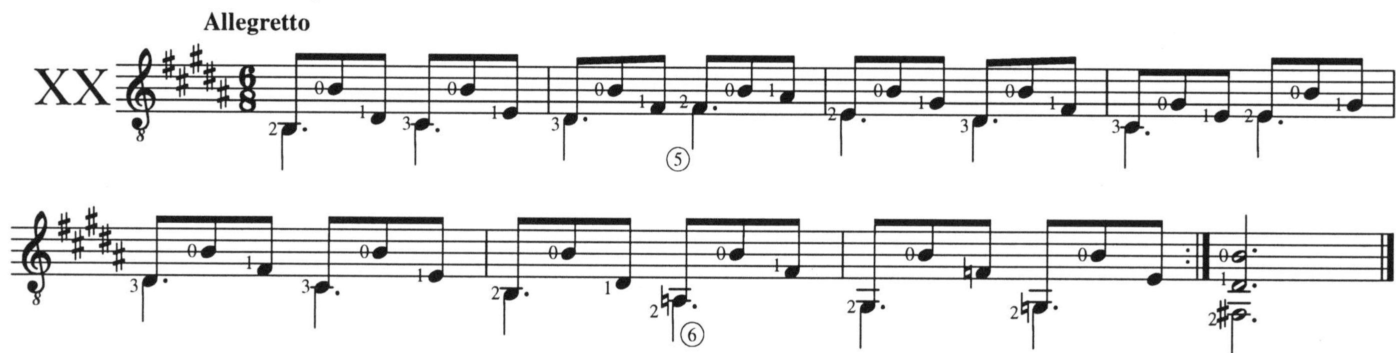

. . . What a beautiful new pink and blue bike resplendent with gleaming chrome, even to the training wheels!

Piece of Eight . . .

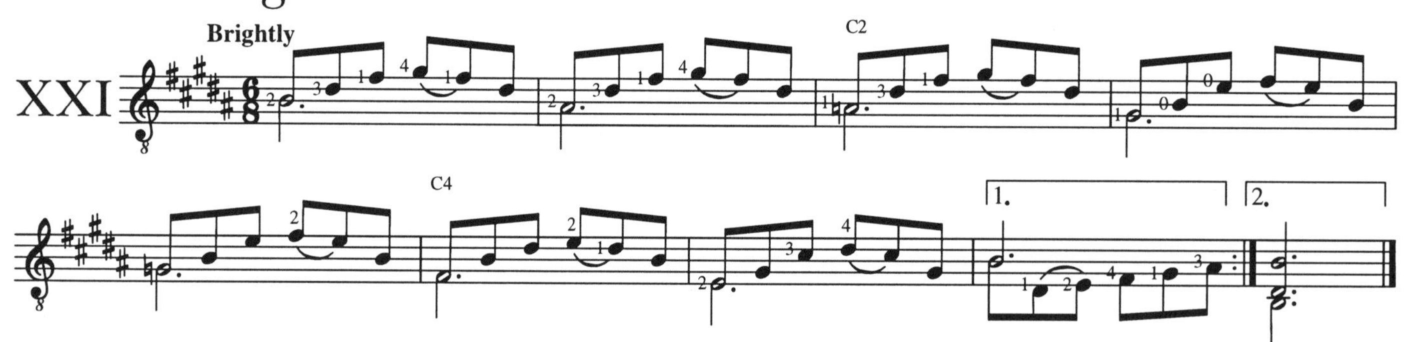

. . . The name of this old Spanish coin conjures up images of pirate ships, buccaneers, bottles of rum, and buried treasure chests on sandy beaches, sans high-rise hotels.

The Arboretum in Autumn . . .

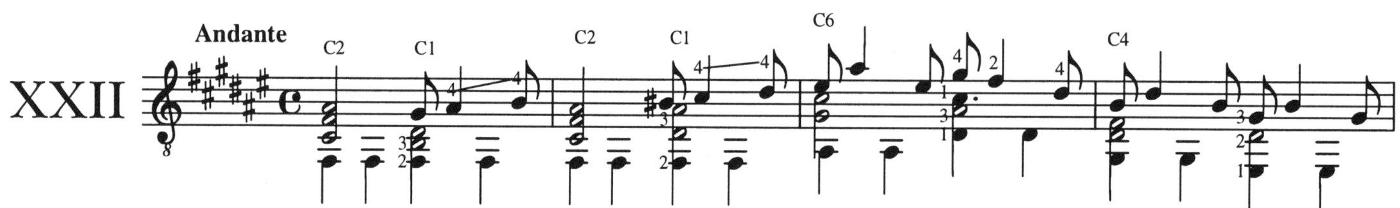

. . . One of the trails in the arboretum is lined with towering maples forming an arcade of golden boughs. Sunlight pours through the canopy creating circles resembling bright coins scattered on the pathway.

August Nocturne . . .

. . . The lake, mirror-like, reflects orange light from the huge full moon. Not a surface ripple appears in this north country lake on an incomparable night which rarely occurs, but never is forgotten.

October Song . . .

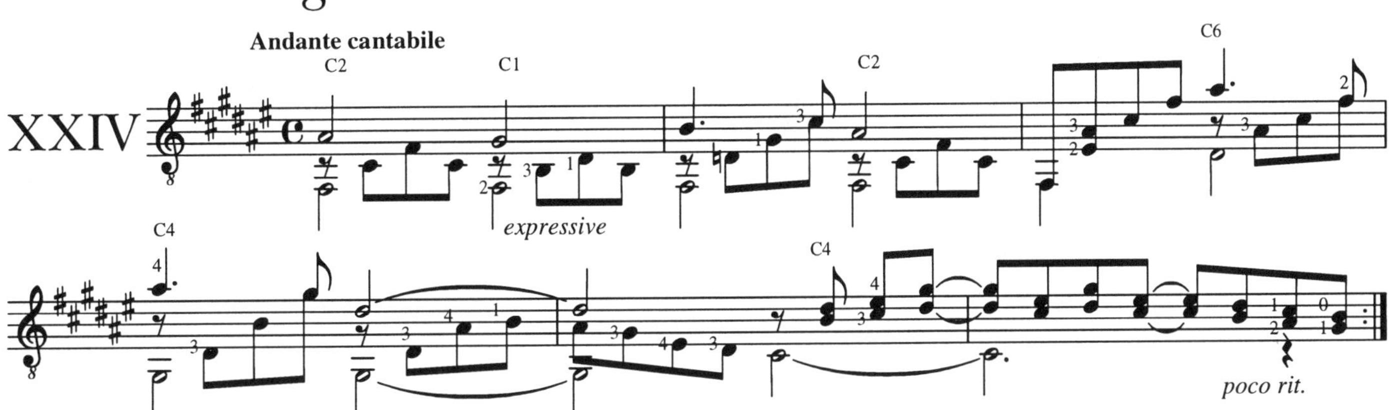

. . . A subtle softly flowing verse, painting with a "Midas touch" the waning days of Autumn.

Day's End . . .

. . . The simple satisfaction at the end of a day well spent with projects completed and neatly in place.

A Second View from A Hill . . .

Note: This Interlude may be used as a direct modulation from Interlude II in C major.

. . . Coming full circle to view again the palette of colors on the vast panorama of Dakota wheatlands.

Fragments . . .

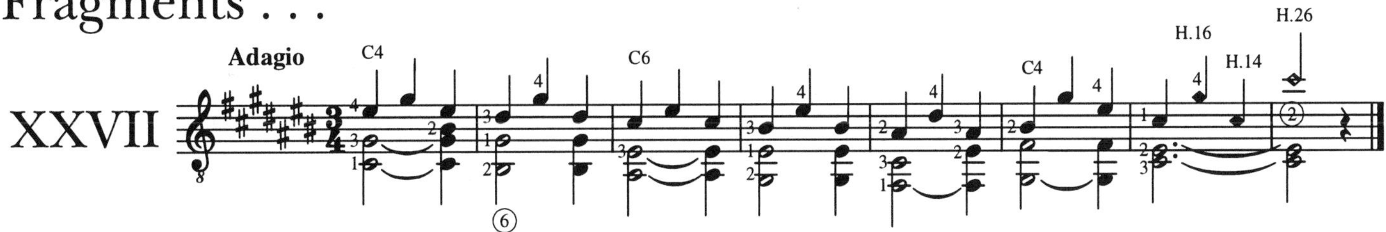

. . . A fleeting memory of persons and places which unbidden,
floats to the surface of the mind from a passing scent, sound or mood.

Flat keys

Morning Mist . . .

. . . A blanket of mist over sleeping field and forest
is drawn silently away by the flrst rays at dawn.

Peregrinations . . .

. . . Strolling about this small Western town with its sidewalks of wood and
unpaved streets weaves an illusion of time traveled back to frontier days.

From a Canoe . . .

. . . Never lifting the paddle from the still waters, so not to disturb but to quietly observe, nesting loons in an island cove.

Lullaby for Mandy . . .

. . . A golden palomino mare whose slender legs, white mane and tail, whose boundless energy yet sweet temperament attest to her largely Arabian heritage.

A Badlands Cameo . . .

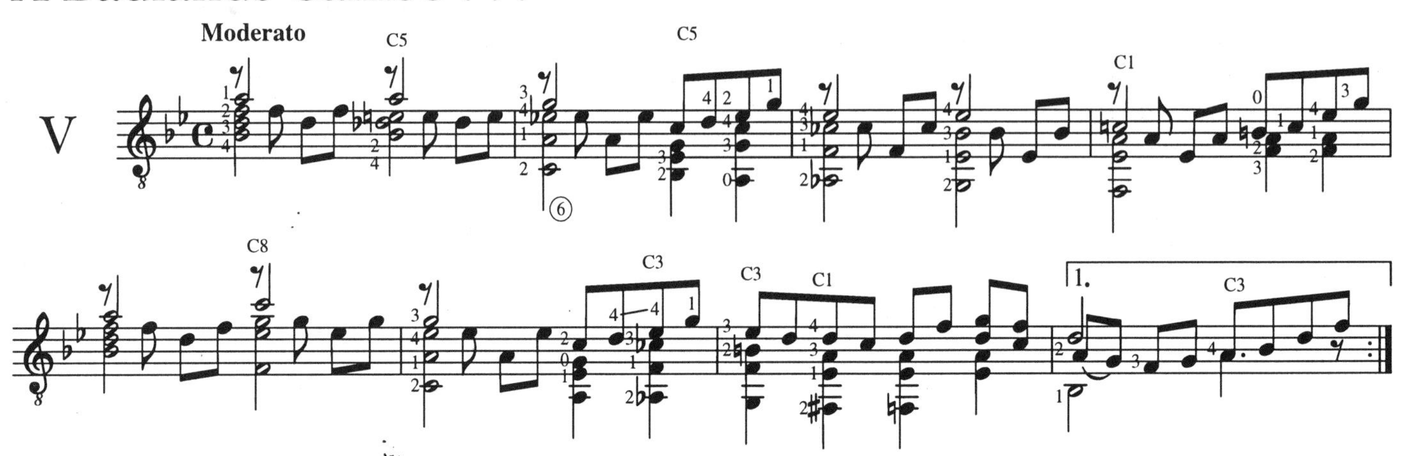

. . . An old-fashioned cameo set in the North Dakota badlands; the chateau of the marquis de Mores overlooks Medora, the historic town, this enterprising French aristocrat established in April of 1883.

Ski Trails . . .

. . . Gently swaying on a chair lift, high above returning skiers, provides a perspective of varied trails and slopes. The longest trail meanders through groves of pine, allowing time to savor the return, as long as possible.

After-thoughts . . .

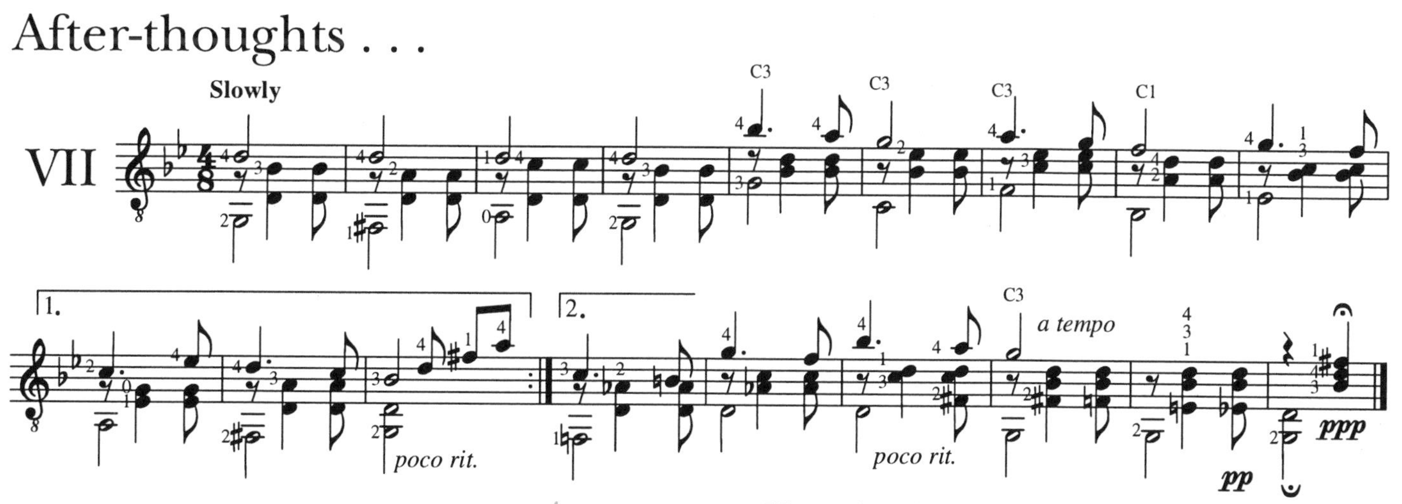

. . . How often impulsive, yet sincere gestures, may in retrospect seem impertinent and intrusive when removed from the circumstance of the moment.

Pleasant Prospects . . .

. . . The anticipation of meeting dear friends for special occasion creates an atmosphere of euphoria.

Dearest Events . . .

. . . "The dearest events are summer rain, and we the para coats that shed every drop." Ralph Waldo Emerson, from *Experience.*

In a Mandan Council Lodge . . .

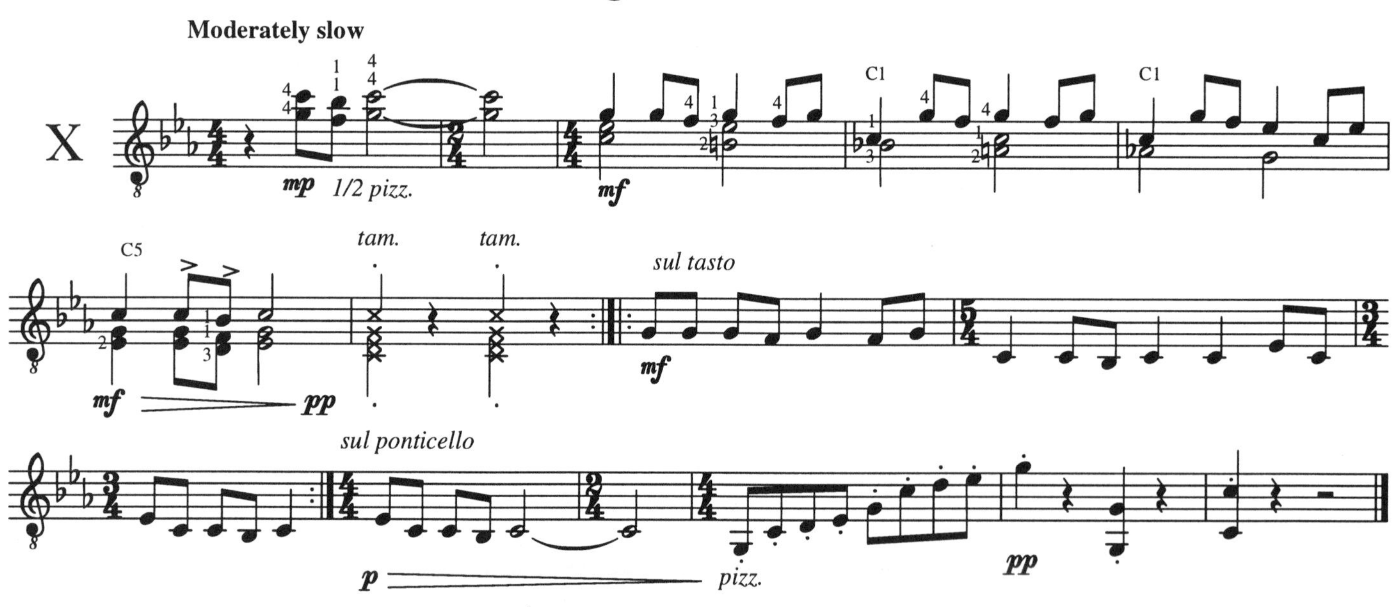

. . . The Mandans constructed beautiful permanent earthen lodges with a central Council Lodge, the largest structure, the center of which was supported by the trunk of a tall lodgepole pine.

Endeavors . . .

. . . "We do what we must, and call it by the best names we can, and would fain have the praise of having intended the result which ensues." Ralph Waldo Emerson, from *Experience.*

Wandering . . .

. . . Meandering over fields and byways in the evening haze of warm summer days, brings peace of mind and a sense of belonging with Nature's own community.

A Touch of Blue . . .

*) Note:

Implies a "swing-feel" style of playing, wherein a triplet is either played or felt on each beat. Commonly derscribed by the term "twelve-feel," viz., a 12/8 measure. This style of playing and interpretation is practiced by jazz, swing and blues musicians.

. . . The distinctive quality of blues melodies is the result of the alteration (flatting) of the third, fifth, and seventh degrees of the Major scale. The principal chords (I, IV, V7) traditionally form the rhythmic accompaniment.

The Chapel . . .

. . . A few paces from the fortressed pioneer settlement, a rough hewn chapel stands, unprotected. Inside a dais with gilded white pulpit and lectern and a carved reed organ face but six pews to hold scarcely more than twenty parishioners.

Echoes At dawn . . .

. . . The slightest sound softly resounds in the stillness that prefaces over forest and field at break of day.

The Lonely Woods . . .

. . . Snow is falling in the lonely woods, a time to lose oneself in the somber beauty of barren trees and tread on crackling ice-laced leaves beneath the crusted snow.

Pleasant Encounters . . .

. . . Those rare occasions while traveling, one meets persons whose warmth and hospitality are a pleasant surprise, and though never met before or ever again are never forgotten.

Woodland Lake . . .

. . . A nameless, jewel-like lake, not much wider than a pond, appears as a surprise nestled as it is deep in Northern woods.

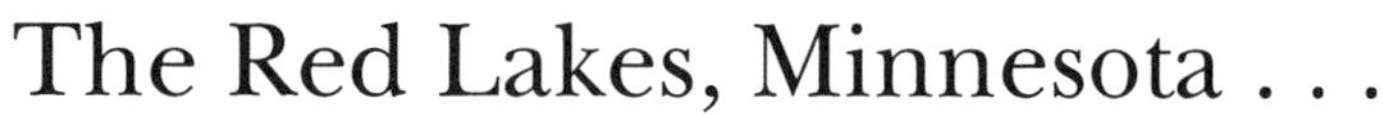

The Red Lakes, Minnesota . . .

. . . Unspoiled by any encroachment by civilization, the Upper and Lower Red Lakes with narrow shores of sand, cattails, and rushes have a prevailing primeval atmosphere, with water so clear it is hard to detect where land and water meet.

Along the Shore . . .

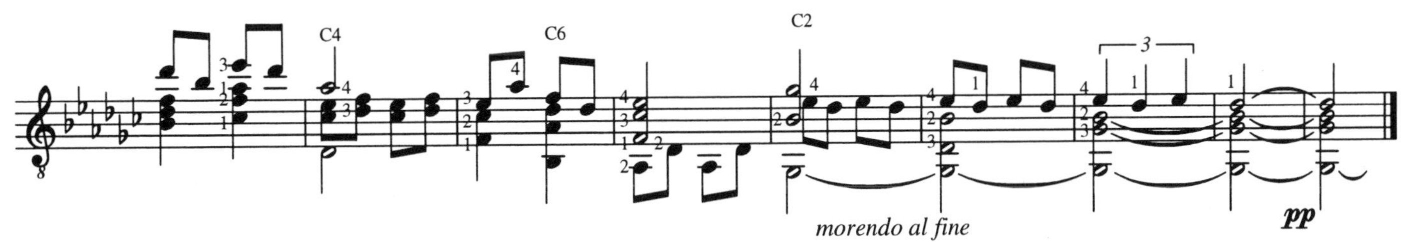

. . . Across the Upper Red Lake, purple storm clouds with a sudden break sends a streak of brilliant sunlight on the lake's horizon.

Tripping the Minuet . . .

. . . With cautious step and inane badinage, we trip a compliant Minuet with those tendentious creatures whose fragile sensitivities are ripe to be offended by the slightest *faux pas.*

Western Hills . . .

. . . Smoothly sculptured hills form a palette of pastels of olive green, deep yellow, pale chrome green, and light ocher blended seamless from shade to shade under a cloudless Western sky.

Achievement . . .

Moderato

XXIII

C9 C5 C2

rit.

a tempo

C4

C2 C4

meno mosso

molto rit.

. . . "The reward for a thing well done is to have done it."
Ralph Waldo Emerson, from *New England Reformers.*